W9-AJU-364

One Hundred Best Poems

for

Boys and Girls

By

Dorothy Aldis
Hilaire Belloc
Mildred Bowers
Gelett Burgess
Hilda Conkling
Emily Dickinson
A. E.
Eleanor Farjeon
Eugene Field
Robert Frost
Oliver Hereford
A. E. Housman
Joyce Kilmer
Rudyard Kipling
Vachel Lindsay
Amy Lowell
Marjorie Barrows
Katharine Lee Bates
Charles E. Carryl
Padraic Colum
Henry van Dyke
John Farrar
Aileen Fisher
Rose Fyleman
Ralph Hodgson
E. L. M. King
Edward Lear
Walter de la Mare
John Masefield
Joaquin Miller
Christopher Morley
Alfred Noyes
Psalm of Praise
Beatrice Curtis Brown
Mary Carolyn Davies
Rachel Lyman Field
Florence Page Jaques
Henry W. Longfellow
Mildred Plew Merryman
James Whitcomb Riley
Elizabeth Madox Roberts
Carl Sandburg
Robert Louis Stevenson
James Stephens
Nancy Byrd Turner
Margaret Widdemer
Dixie Willson
Annette Wynne
William Butler Yeats

Compiled By Marjorie Barrows
Editor "Child Life"

Illustrated by Paula Rees Good

WHITMAN PUBLISHING COMPANY
RACINE, WISCONSIN

To My Mother

Whitman Publishing Company
Racine, Wisconsin

Printed in U. S. A.

ACKNOWLEDGMENTS

The editor wishes to thank the following authors and publishers for permission to include the following poems:

D. Appleton and Company for *The Duck*, *Cobwebs* and *Breadmaking* by E. L. M. King from *50 Country Rhymes for Children.*

The Bobbs-Merrill Company for *The Raggedy Man* and *Little Orphant Annie* by James Whitcomb Riley from *Rhymes of Childhood*, copyright 1890-1926.

Dodd, Mead and Company, Inc. for *Loveliest of Trees* by A. E. Housman from *A Shropshire Lad.*

Doubleday, Doran and Company, Inc. for *Song for a Little House* and *Animal Crackers* by Christopher Morley from *Chimneysmoke*, (copyright, 1917); and *Trees* by Joyce Kilmer from *Trees and Other Poems* (copyright 1914); *Yesterday in Oxford Street*, and *A Fairy went a-Marketing*, by Rose Fyleman from *Fairies and Chimneys* (copyright, 1923); *Taxis*, *General Store*, *Barefoot Days*, *The Animal Store* and *The Playhouse Key* by Rachel Field from *Taxis and Toadstools*, and *Seal Lullaby* from *The Jungle Book*, (copyright 1893, and 1894,) by Rudyard Kipling and reprinted also by permission of Messrs. A. P. Watt and Son, Agents.

E. P. Dutton and Company, for *The Night Will Never Stay* by Eleanor Farjeon from *Gypsy and Ginger.*

Harcourt, Brace and Company, Inc. for *The Bear Hunt*, *The Procession*, *The Family Dragon* and *The Secret Cavern* by Margaret Widdemer from *Little Boy and Girl Land*, (Copyright 1924), also for *Splinter* by Carl Sandburg from *Good Morning, America.*

Harr Wagner Publishing Company for *Columbus* by Joaquin Miller from *Autobiography and Favorite Poems.*

Henry Holt and Company for *Someone*, *The Ship of Rio*, *Silver*, *Dream Song* and *The Linnet* by Walter de la Mare from *Collected Poems*, also for *Stopping by Woods on a Snowy Evening* by Robert Frost from *New Hampshire.*

Houghton Mifflin Company for *Sea Shell* and *The Crescent Moon* by Amy Lowell from *A Dome of Many-Coloured Glass*; *Robinson Crusoe's Story* and *A Nautical Ballad* by Charles E. Carryl from *Davy and the Goblin.*

Alfred A. Knopf, Inc. and Messrs. Gerald Duckworth and Company, Ltd. for *The Yak*, *The Lion*, *The Frog* and *The Gnu* by Hilaire Belloc from *Bad Child's Book of Beasts.*

The Lark and Gelett Burgess for *The Purple Cow.*

Little, Brown and Company for *The Duck and the Kangaroo, The Table and the Chair* and *The Owl and the Pussy Cat* by Edward Lear from *Jingles and Limericks*, and *I Never Saw a Moor* by Emily Dickinson from *Complete Poems.*

The Macmillan Company for *Interior* by Padraic Colum from *Wild Earth and Other Poems*, for *The Mysterious Cat* by Vachel Lindsay from *The Congo and Other Poems*, for *Sea Fever*, and *West Wind* by John Masefield from *Selected Poems*, for *Time, You Old Gipsy Man* by Ralph Hodgson from *Poems*, for *The Horse* and *Fifteen Acres* by James Stephens from *The Rocky Road to Dublin*, for *The Lake Isle of Innisfree* by William Butler Yeats from *Selected Poems*, for *The Frolic* by A. E. from *Collected Poems* and for *The Day Before April* by Mary Carolyn Davies from *The Drums in our Street.*

Minton, Balch and Company for *Little, Hiding*, and *Radiator Lions* by Dorothy Aldis from *Everything and Anything.*

Charles Scribner's Sons for *The Sugar Plum Tree, The Dinkey Bird, Norse Lullaby* and *The Duel* by Eugene Field from *A Little Book of Western Verse*, for *Kitten's Night Thoughts* by Oliver Hereford from *Kitten's Garden of Verses*, for *Where Go the Boats*, and *Farewell to the Farm* by Robert Louis Stevenson from *A Child's Garden of Verses* and for *America for Me* by Henry van Dyke from *Poems of Henry van Dyke.*

Frederick A. Stokes Company for *A Song of Sherwood* by Alfred Noyes from *Collected Poems*, for *Chickadee* by Hilda Conkling from *Poems by a Little Girl*, for *The Pilgrims Came, The Little Tiger Cat* and *Indian Children*, by Annette Wynne from *For Days and Days*, for *Circus* and *Sweetstuff Wife* by Eleanor Farjeon from *Joan's Door*, (copyright, 1927).

The Viking Press, Inc. for *The Circus, Firefly, Christmas Morning, The Woodpecker* and *The Hens* by Elizabeth Madox Roberts from *Under the Tree*, (copyright, 1922, B. W. Huebsch, Inc.)

Yale University Press for *Doorbells, Roads, Gypsies, The Little Rose Tree* and *Rain in the City* by Rachel Lyman Field from *The Pointed People* and for *Serious Omission* by John Farrar from *Songs for Parents.*

Child Life Magazine and the authors for *Finding Fairies, Pine Tree Song* and *The Cricket* by Marjorie Barrows, for *Little Girl Next Door* by Mildred Bowers, for *Jonathan Bing* by Beatrice Curtis Brown, for *The Snowman's Resolution, Down in the Hollow, Otherwise* and *Somersaults* by Aileen Fisher, for *A Goblinade* and *The Puffin* by Florence Page Jaques, for *The Pirate Don Durk, The Moon Song* and *Silver Ships* by Mildred Plew Merryman, for *Lincoln* and *Washington* by Nancy Byrd Turner and for *The Mist and All* and *Politely* by Dixie Willson.

The Day before April

Mary Carolyn Davies

The day before April
  Alone, alone,
I walked in the woods
  And sat on a stone.

I sat on a broad stone
  And sang to the birds.
The tune was God's making
  But I made the words.

Cobwebs

E. L. M. King

Between me and the rising sun,
This way and that the cobwebs run;
Their myriad wavering lines of light
Dance up the hill and out of sight.

There is no land possesses half
So many lines of telegraph
As those the spider-elves have spun
Between me and the rising sun.

Barefoot Days

Rachel Field

In the morning, very early,
  That's the time I love to go
Barefoot where the fern grows curly
  And grass is cool between each toe,
    On a summer morning-O!
    On a summer morning!

That is when the birds go by
  Up the sunny slopes of air,
And each rose has a butterfly
  Or a golden bee to wear;
And I am glad in every toe—
    Such a summer morning-O!
    Such a summer morning!

Roads

Rachel Field

A road might lead to anywhere—
  To harbor towns and quays,
Or to a witch's pointed house
  Hidden by bristly trees.

It might lead past the tailor's door,
  Where he sews with needle and thread,
Or by Miss Pim the milliner's,
  With her hats for every head.
It might be a road to a great, dark cave
  With treasure and gold piled high,
Or a road with a mountain tied to its end,
  Blue-humped against the sky.
Oh, a road might lead you anywhere—
  To Mexico or Maine.
But then, it might just fool you, and—
  Lead you back home again!

Hiding

Dorothy Aldis

I'm hiding, I'm hiding,
And no one knows where;
For all they can see is my
Toes and my hair.

And I just heard my father
Say to my mother—
"But, darling, he must be
Somewhere or other;

"Have you looked in the ink well?"
And Mother said, "Where?"
"In the INK WELL," said Father. But
I was not there.

Then, "Wait!" cried my mother—
"I think that I see
Him under the carpet." But
It was not me.

"Inside the mirror's
A pretty good place,"
Said Father and looked, but saw
Only his face.

"We've hunted," sighed Mother,
"As hard as we could
And I AM so afraid that we've
Lost him for good."

Then I laughed out aloud
And I wiggled my toes
And Father said—"Look, dear,
I wonder if those

Toes could be Benny's.
There are ten of them. See?"
And they WERE so surprised to find
Out it was me!

Little Tiger Cat

Annette Wynne

Little Tiger Cat with the spotted face,
Do you think you've found a baby-jungle-
place?
Going through the grass, stealthily and slow,
Are you waiting to jump out and scare the
folks you know?
And send them running to the house as fast
as they can go?

Little Tiger Cat, it's no use at all,
No matter what you think yourself, you're
rather tame and small,
And with all your hiding and your stern con-
templation,
You cannot scare a single one of high or
lowly station,
And so, there's no use trying to be like your
wild relation.

The Animal Store

Rachel Field

If I had a hundred dollars to spend,
  Or maybe a little more,
I'd hurry as fast as my legs would go
  Straight to the animal store.

I wouldn't say, "How much for this or
    that?"
  "What kind of a dog is he?"
I'd buy as many as rolled an eye,
  Or wagged a tail at me!

I'd take the hound with the drooping ears
  That sits by himself alone;
Cockers and Cairns and wobbly pups
  For to be my very own.

I might buy a parrot all red and green,
  And the monkey I saw before,
If I had a hundred dollars to spend,
  Or maybe a little more.

The Circus

Elizabeth Madox Roberts

Friday came and the circus was there,
And Mother said that the twins and I
And Charles and Clarence and all of us
Could go out and see the parade go by.

And there were wagons with pictures on,
And you never could guess what they had inside,
Nobody could guess, for the doors were shut,
And there was a dog that a monkey could ride.

A man on the top of a sort of cart
Was clapping his hands and making a talk.
And the elephant came—he can step pretty far—
It made us laugh to see him walk.

Three beautiful ladies came riding by,
And each one had on a golden dress,
And each one had a golden whip.
They were queens of Sheba, I guess.

A big wild man was in a cage,
And he had some snakes going over his feet.
And somebody said, "He eats them alive!"
But I didn't see him eat.

General Store

Rachel Field

Some day I'm going to have a store
With a tinkly bell hung over the door,
With real glass cases and counters wide
And drawers all spilly with things inside.
There'll be a little of everything:
Bolts of calico; balls of string;
Jars of peppermint; tins of tea;
Pots and kettles and crockery;
Seeds in packets; scissors bright;
Kegs of sugar, brown and white;
Sarsaparilla for picnic lunches,
Bananas and rubber boots in bunches.
I'll fix the window and dust each shelf,
And take the money in all myself.
It will be my store and I will say:
"What can I do for you today?"

Bread Making

E. L. M. King

Mother's kneading, kneading dough,
In and out her knuckles go;
Till the sticky, shapeless lump
Grows a pillow, smooth and plump.

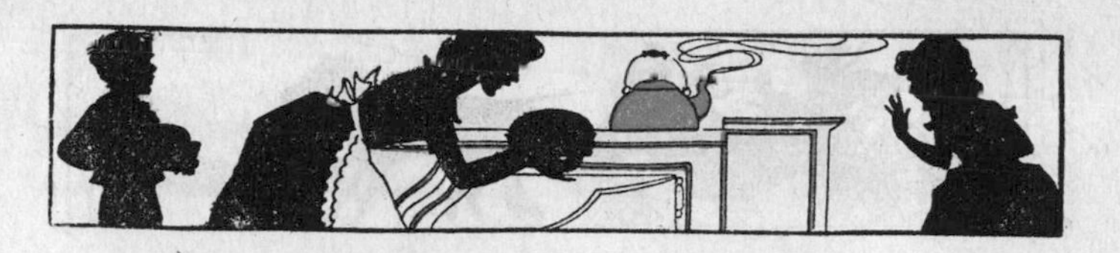

Then she cuts it, pops it in
To the neatly buttered tin,
Leaves it rising high and higher,
While she goes to make the fire.

How the glad flames leap and roar,
Through the open oven-door;
Till their hot breath, as they play,
Makes us wink and run away.

When they've burnt to embers red
Mother shovels in the bread;
And that warm, delicious smell
Tells her it is baking well.

When it's golden, just like wheat,
We shall get a crust to eat;
How I wish we could be fed
Every day on new-made bread!

Farewell to the Farm

Robert Louis Stevenson

The coach is at the door at last;
The eager children, mounting fast
And kissing hands, in chorus sing:
"Good-bye, good-bye, to everything!

"To house and garden, field and lawn,
The meadow-gates we swang upon,
To pump and stable, tree and swing,
Good-bye, good-bye, to everything!

"And fare you well for evermore,
O ladder at the hayloft door,
O hayloft where the cobwebs cling,
Good-bye, good-bye, to everything!"

Crack goes the whip, and off we go;
The trees and houses smaller grow;
Last, round the woody turn we swing:
"Good-bye, good-bye, to everything!"

The Duck

E. L. M. King

If I were in a fairy tale,
And it were my good luck
To have a wish, I'd choose to be
A lovely snow-white duck.

When she puts off into the pond
And leaves me on the brink,
She wags her stumpy tail at me,
And gives a saucy wink,

Which says as plain as words could say,
I'm safe as safe can be,
Stay there, or you will drown yourself.
The pond was made for me.

She goes a-sailing to and fro,
Just like a fishing boat,
And steers and paddles all herself,
And never wets her coat.

Then in the water, upside down,
I've often seen her stand
More neatly than the little boys
Who do it on the land.

And best of all, her children are
The ducklings, bright as gold,
Who swim about the pond with her
And do as they are told.

The Horse

James Stephens

A sparrow hopped about the street,
And he was not a bit afraid;
He flew between a horse's feet,
And ate his supper undismayed:
I think myself the horse knew well
The bird came for the grains that fell.

For his eye was looking down,
  And he danced the corn about
In his nose-bag, till the brown
  Grains of corn were tumbled out;
And I fancy that he said,
"Eat it up, young Speckle-Head!"

The driver then came back again,
  He climbed into the heavy dray;
And he tightened up the rein,
  Cracked his whip and drove away.
But when the horse's ribs were hit,
The sparrow did not care a bit.

Little

Dorothy Aldis

I am the sister of him
And he is my brother.
He is too little for us
To talk to each other.

So every morning I show him
My doll and my book;
But every morning he still is
Too little to look.

Serious Omission

John Farrar

I know that there are dragons,
St. George's, Jason's, too,
And many modern dragons
With scales of green and blue;

But though I've been there many times
And carefully looked through,
I can't find a dragon
In the cages at the zoo!

Doorbells

Rachel Field

You never know with a doorbell
  Who may be ringing it—
It may be Great-Aunt Cynthia
  To spend the day and knit;
It may be a peddler with things to sell
  (I'll buy some when I'm older),
Or the grocer's boy with his apron on
  And a basket on his shoulder;

It may be the old umbrella-man
Giving his queer, cracked call,
Or a lady dressed in rustly silk,
With card-case and parasol.
Doorbells are like a magic game,
Or the grab-bag at a fair—
You never know when you hear one ring
Who may be waiting there!

Song for a Little House

Christopher Morley

I'm glad our house is a little house,
Not too tall nor too wide:
I'm glad the hovering butterflies
Feel free to come inside.

Our little house is a friendly house,
It is not shy or vain;
It gossips with the talking trees
And makes friends with the rain.

And quick leaves cast a shimmer of green
Against our whited walls,
And in the phlox, the courteous bees
Are paying duty calls.

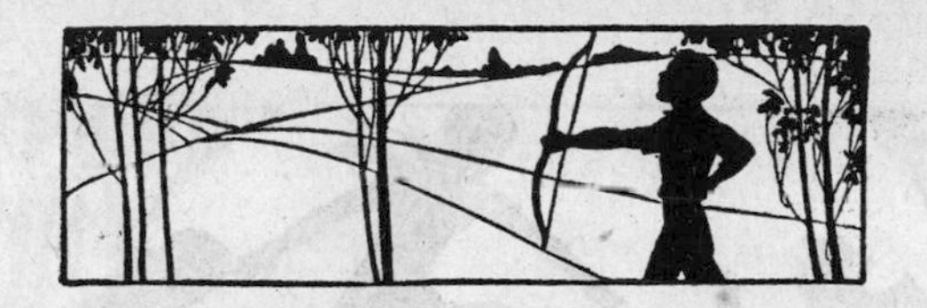

Indian Children

Annette Wynne

Where we walk to school each day
Indian children used to play—
All about our native land,
Where the shops and houses stand.

And the trees were very tall,
And there were no streets at all,
Not a church and not a steeple—
Only woods and Indian people.

Only wigwams on the ground,
And at night bears prowling round—
What a different place today
Where we live and work and play!

Where Go the Boats?

Robert Louis Stevenson

Dark brown is the river,
  Golden is the sand,
It flows along forever,
  With trees on either hand.

Green leaves a-floating,
  Castles of the foam,
Boats of mine a-boating—
  Where will all come home?

On goes the river
  And out past the mill,
Away down the valley,
  Away down the hill.

Away down the river,
  A hundred miles or more,
Other little children
  Shall bring my boats ashore.

The Little Rose Tree

Rachel Field

Every rose on the little tree
Is making a different face at me!
Some look surprised when I pass by,
And others droop—but they are shy.
These two whose heads together press
Tell secrets I could never guess.
Some have their heads thrown back to sing,
And all the buds are listening.
I wonder if the gardener knows,
Or if he calls each just a rose?

Sea Shell

Amy Lowell

Sea Shell, Sea Shell,
  Sing me a song, O please!
A song of ships, and sailor men,
    And parrots, and tropical trees,
Of islands lost in the Spanish Main
Which no man ever may find again,
Of fishes and corals under the waves,
And sea-horses stabled in great green caves.
Sea Shell, Sea Shell,
Sing of the things you know so well.

The Secret Cavern

Margaret Widdemer

Underneath the boardwalk, way, way back,
There's a splendid cavern, big and black—
If you want to get there, you must crawl
Underneath the posts and steps and all
When I've finished paddling, there I go—
None of all the other children know!

There I keep my treasures in a box—
Shells and colored glass and queer-shaped rocks,
In a secret hiding-place I've made,
Hollowed out with clamshells and a spade,
Marked with yellow pebbles in a row—
None of all the other children know!

It's a place that makes a splendid lair,
Room for chests and weapons and one chair.
In the farthest corner, by the stones,
I shall have a flag with skulls and bones
And a lamp that casts a lurid glow—
None of all the other children know!

Some time, by and by, when I am grown,
I shall go and live there all alone;
I shall dig and paddle till it's dark,
Then go out and man my pirate bark:
I shall fill my cave with captive foe—
None of all the other children know!

The Family Dragon

(With acknowledgments to Kenneth Grahame)

Margaret Widdemer

Last night there walked across our lawn a
beast we didn't know—
We saw his little footprints marked quite
plainly in the snow.
It might have been an ocelot, or perhaps a
grizzly bear—
We *hoped* it was a dragon, come out walking from its lair;
We didn't want a grown-up one, all fire and
scales and foam,
But just a baby dragonlet that we could carry
home;
We'd keep him in the nursery and give him
a nice name,
And have him for a fam'ly pet, with ribbons
on, quite tame.
We tracked him down the meadow path
and all along the hedge
And there his little footprints stopped close
up beneath the edge,

For there the snow had gone away—there wasn't any track—
And it was tea-time anyway, so both of us went back.
But we shall go some day quite soon and find him in his lair,
And capture him while he's asleep, and tie him up with care,
And we will have the 'spressman come and put him in his wagon
And bring him home to stay with us and be our family dragon!

A Fairy Went A-Marketing

Rose Fyleman

A fairy went a-marketing—
She bought a little fish;
She put it in a crystal bowl
Upon a golden dish.
An hour she sat in wonderment
And watched its silver gleam,
And then she gently took it up
And slipped it in a stream.

A fairy went a-marketing—
  She bought a coloured bird;
It sang the sweetest, shrillest song
  That ever she had heard.
She sat beside its painted cage
  And listened half the day,
And then she opened wide the door
  And let it fly away.

A fairy went a-marketing—
  She bought a winter gown
All stitched about with gossamer
  And lined with thistledown.
She wore it all the afternoon
  With prancing and delight,
Then gave it to a little frog
  To keep him warm at night.

A fairy went a-marketing—
  She bought a gentle mouse
To take her tiny messages,
  To keep her tiny house.
All day she kept its busy feet
  Pit-patting to and fro,
And then she kissed its silken ears,
  Thanked it, and let it go.

Finding Fairies

Marjorie Barrows

When the winds of March are wakening
The crocuses and crickets,
Did you ever find a fairy near
Some budding little thickets,
A-straightening her golden wings and
Combing out her hair?
She's there!
And when she sees you creeping up
To get a closer peek,
She tumbles through the daffodils,
A-playing hide-and-seek,
And creeps into the tulips till
You can't find *where* she's hid?
Mine did!
Have you ever, ever come across
A little toadstool elf
A-reading by a firefly lamp
And laughing to himself,
Or a saucy fairy queen upon
Her favorite dragonfly?
So've I!

It's fun to see a fairy flutter
Off a catkin boat,
And wrap her fairy baby in
A pussywillow coat;
Oh, don't you love the fairies
And their fairy babies, too?
I do!

Somersaults

Aileen Fisher

Bunny turned somersaults;
It was a surprise
To the ivory elephant
With glossy, glassy eyes.

Somersaults . . . somersaults,
Once and once again,
Until the ivory elephant
Had counted more than ten.

Bunny told the elephant,
"I'm happy I'm not you . . .
You can't turn a somersault,
Not even one or two."

And the elephant said,
"Mercy, don't be such a prig,
I could turn a *million*
If my nose weren't quite so big."

Yesterday in Oxford Street

Rose Fyleman

Yesterday in Oxford Street, oh, what d'you
think, my dears?
I had the most exciting time I've had for
years and years;
The buildings looked so straight and tall, the
sky was blue between,
And, riding on a motor-bus, I saw the fairy
queen!

Sitting there upon the rail and bobbing up
and down,
The sun was shining on her wings and on
her golden crown;
And looking at the shops she was, the pretty silks and lace—
She seemed to think that Oxford Street was
quite a lovely place.

And once she turned and looked at me, and
 waved her little hand;
But I could only stare and stare—oh, would
 she understand?
I simply couldn't speak at all, I simply could-
 n't stir,
And all the rest of Oxford Street was just a
 shining blur.

Then suddenly she shook her wings—a bird
 had fluttered by—
And down into the street she looked and up
 into the sky;
And perching on the railing on a tiny fairy
 toe,
She flashed away so quickly that I hardly
 saw her go.

I never saw her any more, altho' I looked all
 day;
Perhaps she only came to peep, and never
 meant to stay:
But oh, my dears, just think of it, just think
 what luck for me,
That she should come to Oxford Street, and
 I be there to see!

Politely

Dixie Willson

When Goldilocks went calling
  On the Little Baby Bear
And spoiled his bowl of porridge
  And sat holes into his chair—
I hope she hurried home again
  For others nice and new
And took them back politely
  To the Baby Bear. Don't you?

The Sweetstuff Wife

Eleanor Farjeon

The Sweetstuff Wife in the queer little shop
  Has four little window-panes
With bottles of bulls-eye and lollipop,
Peardrop, lemon drop, chocolate drop,
  Boxes of gay tin trains,
Comfits of every color too,
With mottos on them, like "I Love You"
And "Do You Love Me?" "Be Kind," "Be
    True,"
  And horses with fluffy manes,
And sawdust dollies with china heads,

And painted tea-sets, and tiny beds,
And balls with quarters of blues and reds,
And butterfly aeroplanes,
And sugar biscuits, and sweet cigars,
And ninepins, and wind-up motor-cars,
And masks and crackers and silver stars
And paper flowers and chains.

Kitten's Night Thoughts

Oliver Hereford

When Human Folk put out the light
And think they've made it dark as night,
A Pussy Cat sees every bit
As well as when the lights are lit.

When Human Folk have gone upstairs
And shed their skins and said their prayers,
And there is no one to annoy,
Then Pussy may her life enjoy.

No human hands to pinch or slap,
Or rub her fur against the nap,
Or throw cold water from a pail,
Or make a handle of her tail.

And so you will not think it wrong,
When she can play the whole night long,
With no one to disturb her play,
That Pussy goes to bed by day.

Circus

Eleanor Farjeon

The brass band blares,
The naphtha flares,
The sawdust smells,
Showmen ring bells,
And oh! right into the circus-ring
Comes such a lovely, lovely thing,
A milk-white pony with flying tress,
And a beautiful lady,
A beautiful lady,
A *beautiful* lady in a pink dress!
The red-and-white clown
For joy tumbles down
Like a pink rose
Round she goes
On her tiptoes
With the pony under—
And then, oh, wonder!
The pony his milk-white tresses droops,
And the beautiful lady,
The *beautiful* lady,
Flies like a bird through the paper hoops!

The red-and-white clown for joy falls dead,
Then he waggles his feet and stands on his
  head,
And the little boys on the twopenny seats
Scream with laughter and suck their sweets.

The Cricket

Marjorie Barrows

And when the rain had gone away
And it was shining everywhere,
I ran out on the walk to play
And found a little bug was there.

And he was running just as fast
As any little bug could run,
Until he stopped for breath at last,
All black and shiny in the sun.

And then he chirped a song to me
And gave his wings a little tug,
And *that's* the way he showed that he
Was very glad to be a bug!

Chickadee

Hilda Conkling

(Written at the age of six)

The chickadee in the appletree
Talks all the time very gently.
He makes me sleepy.
I rock away to the sea-lights.
Far off I hear him talking
The way smooth bright pebbles
Drop into water . . .
Chick-a-*dee-dee-dee* . . .

Down in the Hollow

Aileen Fisher

Down in the hollow,
Not so far away,
I saw a little ladybug
When I went to play,

Swinging on the clover
Up in the air . . .
I wonder if the ladybug
Knew I was there.

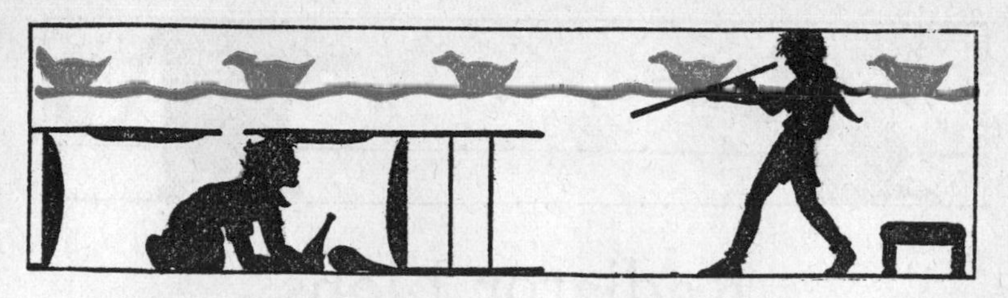

The Bear Hunt

Margaret Widdemer

I played I was two polar bears
Who lived inside a cave of chairs,

And Brother was the hunter-man
Who tried to shoot us when we ran.

The ten-pins made good bones to gnaw,
I held them down beneath my paw.

Of course I had to kill him quick
Before he shot me with his stick,

So all the cave fell down, you see,
On Brother and the bones and me.

So then he said he wouldn't play—
But it was tea-time, anyway!

Little Girl Next Door

Mildred Bowers

If she had a broom straw
Stuck into her hat,
We'd think it was a feather—
She's like that.

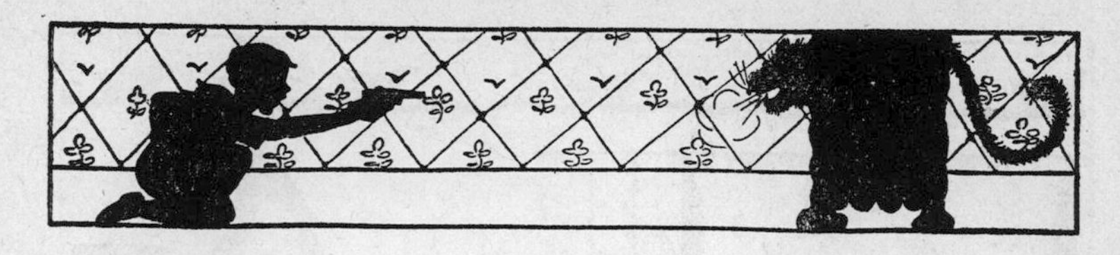

Radiator Lions

Dorothy Aldis

George lives in an apartment and
His mother will not let
Him keep a dog or polliwog
Or rabbit for a pet.

So he has Radiator-Lions.
(The parlor is the zoo.)
They love to fight but will not bite
Unless he tells them to.

And days when it is very cold
And he can't go outdoors
They glower and they lower and they
Crouch upon all fours

And roar most awful roarings and
Gurgle loud and mad.
Up their noses water goeses—
That's what makes them bad.

But he loves Radiator-Lions!
He's glad, although they're wild,
He hasn't dogs and polliwogs
Like any other child!

Taxis

Rachel Field

Ho, for taxis green or blue,
  Hi, for taxis red,
They roll along the Avenue
  Like spools of colored thread!

Jack-O'-Lantern yellow,
Orange as the moon,
Greener than the greenest grass
Ever grew in June.

Gaily striped or checked in squares,
Wheels that twinkle bright,
Don't you think that taxis make
A very pleasant sight?

Taxis shiny in the rain,
Scudding through the snow,
Taxis flashing back the sun,
Waiting in a row.

Ho, for taxis red and green,
  Hi, for taxis blue,
I wouldn't be a private car
  In sober black, would you?

The Mist and All

Dixie Willson

I like the fall,
The mist and all.
I like the night owl's
Lonely call—
And wailing sound
Of wind around.

I like the gray
November day,
And bare, dead boughs
That coldly sway
Against my pane.
I like the rain.

I like to sit
And laugh at it—
And tend
My cozy fire a bit.
I like the fall—
The mist and all—

The Hens

Elizabeth Madox Roberts

The night was coming very fast;
It reached the gate as I ran past.

The pigeons had gone to the tower of the church
And all the hens were on their perch,

Up in the barn, and I thought I heard
A piece of a little purring word.

I stopped inside, waiting and staying,
To try to hear what the hens were saying.

They were asking something, that was plain,
Asking it over and over again.

One of them moved and turned around,
Her feathers made a ruffled sound,

A ruffled sound, like a bushful of birds,
And she said her little asking words.

She pushed her head close into her wing,
But nothing answered anything.

Animal Crackers

Christopher Morley

Animal crackers, and cocoa to drink,
That is the finest of suppers, I think;
When I'm grown up and can have what I
please
I think I shall always insist upon these.

What do *you* choose when you're offered a
treat?
When Mother says, "What would you like
best to eat?"
Is it waffles and syrup, or cinnamon toast?
It's cocoa and animals that *I* love the most!

The kitchen's the cosiest place that I know:
The kettle is singing, the stove is aglow,
And there in the twilight, how jolly to see
The cocoa and animals waiting for me.

Daddy and Mother dine later in state,
With Mary to cook for them, Susan to wait;
But they don't have nearly as much fun as I
Who eat in the kitchen with Nurse standing
by;
And Daddy once said he would like to be me
Having cocoa and animals once more for tea!

The Pilgrims Came

Annette Wynne

The Pilgrims came across the sea,
And never thought of you and me;
And yet it's very strange the way
We think of them Thanksgiving Day.

We tell their story, old and true,
Of how they sailed across the blue,
And found a new land to be free
And built their homes quite near the sea.

Every child knows well the tale
Of how they bravely turned the sail,
And journeyed many a day and night,
To worship God as they thought right.

The people think that they were sad,
And grave; I'm sure that they were glad—
They made Thanksgiving Day—that's fun—
We thank the Pilgrims, every one!

The Woodpecker

Elizabeth Madox Roberts

The woodpecker pecked out a little round hole
And made him a house in the telephone pole.
One day when I watched he poked out his head,
And he had on a hood and a collar of red.
When the streams of rain pour out of the sky,
And the sparkles of lightning go flashing by.
And the big, big wheels of thunder roll,
He can snuggle back in the telephone pole.

Pine Tree Song

Marjorie Barrows

Little pines upon the hill,
Sleeping in the moonlight still,
Are you dreaming now of me
Who bloomed into a Christmas tree?
Baby moons of gold and red
Cuddle close beside my head;
In my tangled leaves a string
Of fairy stars are glimmering;
While my arms, for girls and boys,
Blossom with a hundred toys.
O, little pines, it's fun to live
To be a Christmas tree—and give.

Otherwise

Aileen Fisher

There must be magic,
Otherwise,
How could day turn to night?
And how could sailboats,
Otherwise,
Go sailing out of sight?
And how could peanuts,
Otherwise,
Be covered up so tight?

The Night Will Never Stay

Eleanor Farjeon

The night will never stay,
The night will still go by,
Though with a million stars
You pin it to the sky,
Though you bind it with the blowing wind
And buckle it with the moon,
The night will slip away
Like sorrow or a tune.

The Crescent Moon

Amy Lowell

Slipping softly through the sky,
  Little horned, happy moon,
Can you hear me up so high?
  Will you come down soon?

On my nursery window-sill
  Will you stay your steady flight?
And then float away with me
  Through the summer night?

Brushing over tops of trees,
  Playing hide and seek with stars,
Peeping up through shiny clouds
  At Jupiter or Mars.

I shall fill my lap with roses
  Gathered in the milky way,
All to carry home to mother.
  Oh! what will she say!

Little rocking, sailing moon,
  Do you hear me shout—Ahoy!
Just a little nearer, moon,
  To please a little boy.

The Playhouse Key

Rachel Field

This is the key to the playhouse
  In the woods by the pebbly shore,
It's winter now; I wonder if
  There's snow about the door?

I wonder if the fir trees tap
  Green fingers on the pane
If sea gulls cry and the roof is wet
  And tinkle-y with rain?

I wonder if the flower-sprigged cups
  And plates sit on their shelf,
And if my little painted chair
  Is rocking by itself?

Gypsies

Rachel Field

Last night the gypsies came—
Nobody knows from where.
Where they've gone to nobody knows,
And nobody seems to care!

Between the trees on the old swamp road
I saw them round their fire:

Tattered children and dogs that barked
As the flames leaped high and higher;
There were black-eyed girls in scarlet shawls,
Old folk wrinkled with years,
Men with handkerchiefs round their throats
And silver loops in their ears.
Ragged and red like maple leaves
When frost comes in the fall,
The gypsies stayed but a single night;
In the morning gone were all—
Never a shaggy gypsy dog.
Never a gypsy child;
Only a burnt-out gypsy fire
Where danced that band so wild.

All gone and away,
Who knows where?
Only the wind that sweeps
Maple branches bare.

The Snowman's Resolution

Aileen Fisher

The snowman's hat was crooked
  And his nose was out of place
And several of his whiskers
  Had fallen from his face.

But the snowman didn't notice
  For he was trying to think
Of a New Year's resolution
  That wouldn't melt or shrink.

He thought and planned and pondered
  With his little snow-ball head
Till his eyes began to glisten
  And his toes began to spread;

And at last he said, "I've got it—
  I'll make a firm resolve
That no matter what the weather
  My smile will not dissolve."

Now the snowman acted wisely
  And his resolution won
For his splinter smile was *wooden*
  And it didn't mind the sun!

Little Orphant Annie

James Whitcomb Riley

Little Orphant Annie's come to our house
to stay,
An' wash the cups and saucers up, an' brush
the crumbs away,
An' shoo the chickens off the porch, an'
dust the hearth, an' sweep,
An' make the fire, an' bake the bread, an'
earn her board-an'-keep;
An' all us other children, when the supper
things is done,
We set around the kitchen fire an' has the
mostest fun
A-list'nin' to the witch tales 'at Annie tells
about,
An' the Gobble-uns 'at gits you

Ef you
Don't
Watch
Out!

Onc't they was a little boy wouldn't say his
pray'rs—
An' when he went to bed at night, away up-
stairs,
His mammy heerd him holler, an' his daddy
heerd him bawl,
An' when they turn't the kivvers down, he
wasn't there at all!
An' they seeked him in the rafter-room, an'
cubby-hole, an' press,
An' seeked him up the chimbly flue, an' ev-
er'wheres, I guess;
But all they ever found was thist his pants
an' round about!
An' the Gobble-uns 'll git you
Ef you
Don't
Watch
Out!

An' one time a little girl 'ud allus laugh an'
grin,
An' make fun of ever'one an' all her blood-
an'-kin;
An' onc't when they was "company," an'
ole folks was there,
She mocked 'em an' shocked 'em and said
she didn't care!
An' thist as she kicked her heels, an' turn't
to run an' hide,

They was two great big Black Things a-
standin' by her side,
An' they snatched her through the ceilin'
'fore she knowed what she's about!
An' the Gobble-uns 'll git you
Ef you
Don't
Watch
Out!

An' little Orphant Annie says, when the
blaze is blue,
An' the lampwick sputters, an' the wind
goes woo-oo!
An' you hear the crickets quit, an' the
moon is gray,
An' the lightnin'-bugs in dew is all
squenched away—
You better mind yer parents, an' yer teach-
ers fond an' dear,
An' churish them 'at loves you, an' dry the
orphant's tear,
An' he'p the pore an' needy ones 'at cluster
all about,
Er the Gobble-uns 'll git you
Ef you
Don't
Watch
Out!

Hiawatha's Childhood

Henry Wadsworth Longfellow

At the door on summer evenings
Sat the little Hiawatha;
Heard the whispering of the pine-trees,
Heard the lapping of the water,
Sounds of music, words of wonder;
"Minne-wawa!" said the pine-trees,
"Mudway-aushka!" said the water.

Saw the fire-fly, Wah-wah-taysee,
Flitting through the dusk of evening,
With the twinkle of its candle
Lighting up the brakes and bushes,
And he sang the song of children,
Sang the song Nokomis taught him:
"Wah-wah-taysee, little firefly,
Little, flitting, white-fire insect,
Little, dancing, white-fire creature,
Light me with your little candle,
Ere upon my bed I lay me,
Ere in sleep I close my eyelids!"

The Raggedy Man

James Whitcomb Riley

O The Raggedy Man! He works for Pa;
An' he's the goodest man ever you saw!
He comes to our house every day,
An' waters the horses, an' feeds 'em hay;
An' he opens the shed—an' we all ist laugh
When he drives out our little old wobblely
calf;
An' nen—ef our hired girl says he can—
He milks the cow for 'Lizabuth Ann.—
Ain't he a' awful good Raggedy Man?
Raggedy! Raggedy! Raggedy Man!

W'y, The Raggedy Man—he's ist so good
He splits the kindlin' an' chops the wood;
An' nen he spades in our garden, too,
An' does most things 'at boys can't do!—
He clumbed clean up in our big tree
An' shooked a' apple down fer me—
An' nother'n, too, fer 'Lizabuth Ann—
An' nother'n, too, fer The Raggedy Man—
Ain't he a' awful kind Raggedy Man?
Raggedy! Raggedy! Raggedy Man!

An' The Raggedy Man, he knows most
rhymes
An' tells 'em, ef I be good, sometimes:
Knows 'bout Giunts, an' Griffuns, an' Elves,
An' the Squidgicum-Squees 'at swallers ther-
selves!
An', wite by the pump in our pasture-lot,
He showed me the hole 'at the Wunks is got,
'At lives 'way deep in the ground, an' can
Turn into me, er 'Lizabuth Ann!
Ain't he a funny old Raggedy Man?
Raggedy! Raggedy! Raggedy Man!

The Raggedy Man—one time when he
Wuz makin' a little bow-'n'-orry fer me,
Says, "When you're big like your Pa is,
Air you go' to keep a fine store like his—
An' be a rich merchunt—an' wear fine
clothes?—
Er what air you go' to be, goodness knows!"
An' nen he laughed at 'Lizabuth Ann,
An' I says, " 'M go' to be a Raggedy Man!
I'm ist go' to be a nice Raggedy Man!
Raggedy! Raggedy! Raggedy Man!"

Silver

Walter de la Mare

Slowly, silently, now the moon
Walks the night in her silver shoon;
This way, and that, she peers, and sees
Silver fruit upon silver trees;
One by one the casements catch
Her beams beneath the silvery thatch;
Couched in his kennel, like a log,
With paws of silver sleeps the dog;
From their shadowy cote the white breasts
peep
Of doves in a silver-feathered sleep;
A harvest mouse goes scampering by,
With silver claws, and silver eye;
And moveless fish in the water gleam,
By silver reeds in a silver stream.

Dream-Song

Walter de la Mare

Sunlight, moonlight,
Twilight, starlight—
Gloaming at the close of day,
And an owl calling,
Cool dews falling
In a wood of oak and may.

Lantern-light, taper-light,
Torchlight, no-light:
Darkness at the shut of day,
And lions roaring,
Their wrath pouring
In wild waste places far away.

Elf-light, bat-light,
Touchwood-light and toad-light,
And the sea a shimmering gloom of grey,
And a small face smiling
In a dream's beguiling
In a world of wonders far away.

Firefly

(A Song)

Elizabeth Madox Roberts

A little light is going by,
Is going up to see the sky,
A little light with wings.

I never could have thought of it,
To have a little bug all lit
And made to go on wings.

Seal Lullaby

Rudyard Kipling

Oh! hush thee, my baby, the night is behind
us,
And black are the waters that sparkled so
green.
The moon, o'er the combers, looks down-
ward to find us
At rest in the hollows that rustle between.
Where billow meets billow, there soft be thy
pillow;
Ah, weary wee flipperling, curl at thy
ease!
The storm shall not wake thee, nor shark
overtake thee,
Asleep in the arms of the slow-swinging
seas.

Norse Lullaby

Eugene Field

The sky is dark and the hills are white
As the storm-king speeds from the north
tonight;
And this is the song the storm-king sings,
As over the world his cloak he flings:
"Sleep, sleep, little one, sleep;"
He rustles his wings and gruffly sings:
"Sleep, little one, sleep."

On yonder mountain-side a vine
Clings at the foot of a mother pine;
The tree bends over the trembling thing,
And only the vine can hear her sing:
"Sleep, sleep, little one, sleep—
What shall you fear when I am here?
Sleep, little one, sleep."

The king may sing in his bitter flight,
The tree may croon to the vine tonight,
But the little snowflake at my breast
Liketh the song I sing the best—
Sleep, sleep, little one, sleep;
Weary thou art, a-next my heart,
Sleep, little one, sleep.

Moon Song

Mildred Plew Merryman

Zoon, zoon, cuddle and croon—
  Over the crinkling sea,
The moon man flings him a silvered net
  Fashioned of moonbeams three.

And some folk say when the net lies long
  And the midnight hour is ripe;
The moon man fishes for some old song
  That fell from a sailor's pipe.

And some folk say that he fishes the bars
  Down where the dead ships lie,
Looking for lost little baby stars
  That slid from the slippery sky.

And the waves roll out and the waves roll in
  And the nodding night wind blows,
But why the moon man fishes the sea
  Only the moon man knows.

Zoon, zoon, net of the moon
  Rides on the wrinkling sea;
Bright is the fret and shining wet,
  Fashioned of moonbeams three.

And some folk say when the great net gleams
  And the waves are dusky blue,
The moon man fishes for two little dreams
  He lost when the world was new.

And some folk say in the late night hours
While the long fin-shadows slide,
The moon man fishes for cold sea flowers
Under the tumbling tide.

And the waves roll out and the waves roll in
And the gray gulls dip and doze,
But why the moon man fishes the sea
Only the moon man knows.

Zoon, zoon, cuddle and croon—
Over the crinkling sea,
The moon man flings him a silvered net
Fashioned of moonbeams three.

And some folk say that he follows the flecks
Down where the last light flows,
Fishing for two round gold-rimmed "specs"
That blew from his button-like nose.

And some folk say while the salt sea foams
And the silver net lines snare,
The moon man fishes for carven combs
That float from the mermaids' hair.

And the waves roll out and the waves roll in
And the nodding night wind blows,
But why the moon man fishes the sea
Only the moon man knows.

The Procession

Margaret Widdemer

When the snow has gone away
Maypinks blossom where it lay,

And before the Maypink's gone
Dancing windflowers hurry on:

All the violet-buds are made
Long before the windflowers fade

Then before the violets go
Yellow dandelions grow:

And before they ever die
Buttercups are growing high,

Then the daisies hurry up,
Each beside a buttercup:

Little pink wild roses follow,
And in every sunny hollow

Black-eyed Susans grow up tall
Long before the roses fall.

Clovers blossom pink and steady
Till the goldenrod is ready:

Purple asters last of all
Wait until the late, late fall,

Till the snow comes flying down
Once again on field and town.

Flowers are very kind to grow
One by one, and never go

Till the snow comes back, and stays
Here for all our winter plays!

Christmas Morning

Elizabeth Madox Roberts

If Bethlehem were here today,
Or this were very long ago,
There wouldn't be a winter time
Nor any cold or snow.

I'd run out through the garden gate,
And down along the pasture walk;
And off beside the cattle barns
I'd hear a kind of gentle talk.

I'd move the heavy iron chain
And pull away the wooden pin;
I'd push the door a little bit
And tiptoe very softly in.

The pigeons and the yellow hens
And all the cows would stand away;

Their eyes would open wide to see
A lady in the manger hay,

If this were very long ago
And Bethlehem were here today.

And Mother held my hand and smiled—
I mean the lady would—and she
Would take the woolly blankets off
Her little boy so I could see.

His shut-up eyes would be asleep,
And he would look like our John,
And he would be all crumpled too,
And have a pinkish color on.

I'd watch his breath go in and out.
His little clothes would all be white.
I'd slip my finger in his hand
To feel how he could hold it tight.

And she would smile and say, "Take care,"
The mother, Mary, would, "Take care;"
And I would kiss his little hand
And touch his hair.

While Mary put the blankets back
The gentle talk would soon begin.
And when I'd tiptoe softly out
I'd meet the wise men going in.

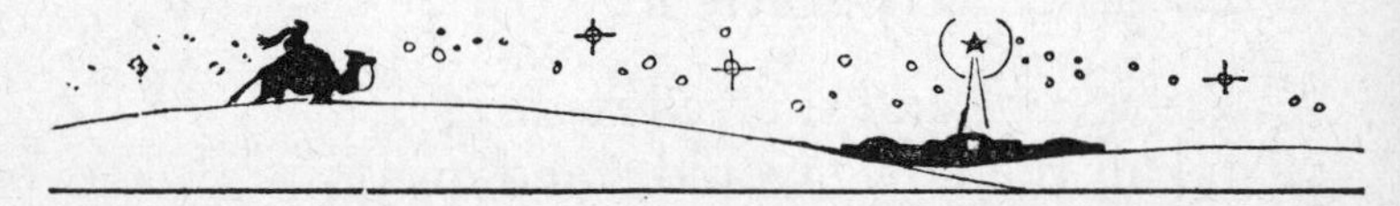

Part II

Jonathan Bing

B. Curtis Brown

Poor old Jonathan Bing
Went out in his carriage to visit the King,
But everyone pointed and said, "Look at that!
Jonathan Bing has forgotten his hat!"
(He'd forgotten his hat!)

Poor old Jonathan Bing
Went home and put on a new hat for the King,
But up by the palace a soldier said, "Hi!
You can't see the King; you've forgotten your tie!"
(He'd forgotten his tie!)

Poor old Jonathan Bing,
He put on a beautiful tie ror the King,
But when he arrived an Archbishop said, "Ho!
You can't come to court in pyjamas, you know!"

Poor old Jonathan Bing
Went home and addressed a short note to the King:
"If you please will excuse me I won't come to tea,
For home's the best place for all people like me!"

Pirate Don Durk of Dowdee

Mildred Plew Merryman

Ho, for the Pirate Don Durk of Dowdee!
He was as wicked as wicked could be,
But oh, he was perfectly gorgeous to see!
The Pirate Don Durk of Dowdee.

His conscience, of course, was as black as a bat,
But he had a floppety plume on his hat
And when he went walking it jiggled—like that!
The plume of the Pirate Dowdee.

His coat it was crimson and cut with a slash,
And often as ever he twirled his mustache
Deep down in the ocean the mermaids went splash,
Because of Don Durk of Dowdee.

Moreover, Dowdee had a purple tattoo,
And stuck in his belt where he buckled it through
Were a dagger, a dirk and a squizzamaroo,
For fierce was the Pirate Dowdee.

So fearful he was he would shoot at a puff,
And always at sea when the weather grew
rough
He drank from a bottle and wrote on his cuff,
Did Pirate Don Durk of Dowdee.

Oh, he had a cutlass that swung at his thigh
And he had a parrot called Pepperkin Pye,
And a zigzaggy scar at the end of his eye
Had Pirate Don Durk of Dowdee.

He kept in a cavern, this buccaneer bold,
A curious chest that was covered with
mould,
And all of his pockets were jingly with gold!
Oh jing! went the gold of Dowdee.

His conscience, of course, it was crook'd like
a squash,
But both of his boots made a slickery slosh,
And he went through the world with a won-
derful swash,
Did Pirate Don Durk of Dowdee.

It's true he was wicked as wicked could be,
His sins they outnumbered a hundred and
three,
But oh, he was perfectly gorgeous to see,
The Pirate Don Durk of Dowdee.

The Mysterious Cat

Vachel Lindsay

I saw a proud, mysterious cat,
I saw a proud, mysterious cat
Too proud to catch a mouse or rat—
Mew, mew, mew.

But catnip she would eat, and purr,
But catnip she would eat, and purr.
And goldfish she did much prefer—
Mew, mew, mew.

I saw a cat—'twas but a dream,
I saw a cat—'twas but a dream,
Who scorned the slave that brought her
cream—
Mew, mew, mew.

Unless the slave were dressed in style
Unless the slave were dressed in style
And knelt before her all the while—
Mew, mew, mew.

Did you ever hear of a thing like that?
Did you ever hear of a thing like that?
Did you ever hear of a thing like that?
Oh, what a proud, mysterious cat.
Oh, what a proud, mysterious cat.
Oh, what a proud, mysterious cat.
Mew . . . mew . . . mew.

The Sugar-Plum Tree

Eugene Field

Have you ever heard of the Sugar-Plum
Tree?
'Tis a marvel of great renown!
It blooms on the shore of the Lollypop Sea
In the garden of Shut-Eye Town;
The fruit that it bears is so wondrously sweet
(As those who have tasted it say)
That good little children have only to eat
Of that fruit to be happy next day.

When you've got to the tree, you would
have a hard time
To capture the fruit which I sing;
The tree is so tall that no person could climb
To the boughs where the sugar-plums
swing!

But up in that tree sits a chocolate cat,
And a gingerbread dog prowls below—
And this is the way you contrive to get at
Those sugar-plums tempting you so:

You say but the word to that gingerbread dog
And he barks with such terrible zest
That the chocolate cat is at once all agog,
As her swelling proportions attest.
And the chocolate cat goes cavorting around
From this leafy limb unto that,
And the sugar-plums tumble, of course, to the ground—
Hurrah for that chocolate cat!

There are marshmallows, gumdrops, and peppermint canes
With stripings of scarlet or gold,
And you carry away of the treasure that rains,
As much as your apron can hold!
So come, little child, cuddle closer to me
In your dainty white nightcap and gown,
And I'll rock you away to that Sugar-Plum Tree
In the garden of Shut-Eye Town.

The Duel

Eugene Field

The gingham dog and the calico cat
Side by side on the table sat;
'Twas half past twelve, and (what do you
think!)
Nor one nor t'other had slept a wink!
The old Dutch clock and the Chinese
plate
Appeared to know as sure as fate
There was going to be a terrible spat.
(*I wasn't there: I simply state*
What was told to me by the Chinese
plate!)

The gingham dog went, "Bow-wow-wow!"
And the calico cat replied, "Mee-ow!"
The air was littered, an hour or so,
With bits of gingham and calico,
While the old Dutch clock in the chimney
place
Up with its hands before its face,
For it always dreaded a family row!

(Now mind: I'm only telling you
What the old Dutch clock declares is
true!)

The Chinese plate looked very blue,
And wailed, "Oh, dear! what shall we do!"
But the gingham dog and the calico cat
Wallowed this way and tumbled that,
Employing every tooth and claw
In the awfullest way you ever saw—
And, oh! how the gingham and calico flew:
(Don't fancy I exaggerate—
I got my news from the Chinese plate!)

Next morning, where the two had sat
They found no trace of dog or cat:
And some folks think unto this day
That burglars stole that pair away!
But the truth about the cat and pup
Is this: they ate each other up!
Now what do you really think of that!
(The old Dutch clock it told me so,
And that is how I came to know.)

There Was Once a Puffin

Florence Page Jaques

Oh, there once was a Puffin
Just the shape of a muffin,
And he lived on an island
In the
        bright
                blue sea!
He ate little fishes,
That were most delicious,
And he had them for supper
And he
        had
                them
                        for tea.
But this poor little Puffin,
He couldn't play nothin',
For he hadn't anybody
To
        play
                with
                        at all.

So he sat on his island,
And he cried for awhile, and
He felt very lonely,
And he
felt
very small.
Then along came the fishes,
And they said, "If you wishes,
You can have us for playmates,
Instead
of
for
tea!"
So they now play together,
In all sorts of weather,
And the puffin eats pancakes,
Like you
and
like
me.

The Duck and the Kangaroo

Edward Lear

Said the Duck to the Kangaroo,
  "Good gracious! how you hop
Over the fields, and the water too,
  As if you never would stop!
My life is a bore in this nasty pond:
And I long to go out in the world beyond:
  I wish I could hop like you."
  Said the Duck to the Kangaroo.

"Please give me a ride on your back,"
  Said the Duck to the Kangaroo:
"I would sit quite still, and say nothing but
    'Quack'
  The whole of the long day through:
And we'd go to the Dee, and the Jelly Bo
    Lee,
Over the land, and over the sea:
  Please take me a ride! oh, do!"
  Said the Duck to the Kangaroo.

Said the Kangaroo to the Duck,
  "This requires some little reflection.
Perhaps, on the whole, it might bring me
    luck;
  And there seems but one objection;
Which is, if you'll let me speak so bold,
Your feet are unpleasantly wet and cold,
  And would probably give me the roo-
  Matiz," said the Kangaroo.

Said the Duck, "As I sat on the rocks,
  I have thought over that completely;
And I bought four pairs of worsted socks,
  Which fit my web-feet neatly;
And, to keep out the cold, I've bought a
    cloak,
And every day a cigar I'll smoke;
  All to follow my own dear true
  Love of a Kangaroo."

Said the Kangaroo, "I'm ready,
  All in the moonlight pale;
But to balance me well, dear Duck, sit steady,
  And quite at the end of my tail."
So away they went with a hop and a bound;
And they hopped the whole world three
    times round.
  And who so happy, oh! who,
  As the Duck and the Kangaroo.

The Owl and the Pussy-Cat

Edward Lear

The Owl and the Pussy-Cat went to sea
  In a beautiful pea-green boat,
They took some honey, and plenty of money,
  Wrapped up in a five-pound note.
The Owl looked up to the stars above,
  And sang to a small guitar,
"O lovely Pussy! O Pussy, my love,
  What a beautiful Pussy you are,
      You are!
  What a beautiful Pussy you are!"

Pussy said to the Owl, "You elegant fowl!
  How charmingly sweet you sing!
O let us be married! too long we have tarried:
  But what shall we do for a ring?"

They sailed away for a year and a day,
To the land where the Bong-tree grows,
And there in a wood a Piggy-wig stood,
With a ring at the end of his nose,
His nose,
With a ring at the end of his nose.

"Dear Pig, are you willing to sell for one shilling
Your ring?" Said the Piggy, "I will."
So they took it away, and were married next day
By the Turkey who lives on the hill.
They dined on mince, and slices of quince,
Which they ate with a runcible spoon;
And hand in hand, on the edge of the sand,
They danced by the light of the moon,
The moon,
They danced by the light of the moon.

The Ship of Rio

Walter de la Mare

There was a ship of Rio
  Sailed out into the blue,
And nine and ninety monkeys
  Were all her jovial crew.
From bos'un to the cabin boy,
  From quarter to caboose,
There weren't a stitch of calico
  To breech 'em—tight or loose;
From spar to deck, from deck to keel,
  From barnacle to shroud,
There weren't one pair of reach-me-downs
  To all that jabbering crowd.
But wasn't it a gladsome sight,
  When roared the deep-sea gales,
To see them reef her fore and aft,
  A-swinging by their tails!
Oh, wasn't it a gladsome sight,
  When glassy calm did come,
To see them squatting tailor-wise
  Around a keg of rum!
Oh, wasn't it a gladsome sight,
  When in she sailed to land,
To see them all a-scampering skip
  For nuts across the sand!

The Dinkey-Bird

Eugene Field

In an ocean, 'way out yonder
  (As all sapient people know),
Is the land of Wonder-Wander,
  Whither children love to go;
It's their playing, romping, swinging,
  That give great joy to me
While the Dinkey-Bird goes singing
  In the amfalula tree!

There the gum-drops grow like cherries
  And taffy's thick as peas—
Caramels you pick like berries
  When, and where, and how you please;
Big red sugar-plums are clinging
  To the cliffs beside that sea
Where the Dinkey-Bird is singing
  In the amfalula tree.

So when children shout and scamper
  And make merry all the day,
When there's naught to put a damper
  To the ardor of their play;
When I hear their laughter ringing,
  Then I'm sure as sure can be
That the Dinkey-Bird is singing
  In the amfalula tree.

For the Dinkey-Bird's bravuras
  And staccatos are so sweet—
His roulades, appoggiaturas,
  And robustos so complete,
That the youth of every nation—
  Be they near or far away—
Have especial delectation
  In that gladsome roundelay.

Their eyes grow bright and brighter—
  Their lungs begin to crow,
Their hearts get light and lighter,
  And their cheeks are all aglow;
For an echo cometh bringing
  The news to all and me,
That the Dinkey-Bird is singing
  In the amfalula tree.

I'm sure you'd like to go there
  To see your feathered friend—
And so many goodies grow there
  You would like to comprehend!
Speed, little dreams, your winging
  To that land across the sea
Where the Dinkey-Bird is singing
  In the amfalula tree!

Robinson Crusoe's Story

Charles Edward Carryl

The night was thick and hazy
When the "Piccadilly Daisy"
Carried down the crew and captain in the sea;
And I think the water drowned 'em;
For they never, never found 'em,
And I know they didn't come ashore with me.

Oh! 'twas very sad and lonely
When I found myself the only
Population on this cultivated shore;
But I've made a little tavern
In a rocky little cavern
And I sit and watch for people at the door.

I spent no time in looking
For a girl to do my cooking,
As I'm quite a clever hand at making stews;
But I had that fellow Friday,
Just to keep the tavern tidy,
And to put a Sunday polish on my shoes.

I have a little garden
That I'm cultivating lard in,
As the things I eat are rather tough and dry;
For I live on toasted lizards,
Prickly pears, and parrot gizzards,
And I'm really very fond of beetle-pie.

The clothes I had were furry,
And it made me fret and worry
When I found the moths were eating off the hair;
And I had to scrape and sand 'em,
And I boiled 'em and I tanned 'em,
Till I got the fine morocco suit I wear.

I sometimes seek diversion
In a family excursion
With the few domestic animals you see;
And we take along a carrot
As refreshment for the parrot,
And a little can of jungleberry tea.

Then we gather as we travel,
Bits of moss and dirty gravel,
And we chip off little specimens of stone;
And we carry home as prizes
Funny bugs, of handy sizes,
Just to give the day a scientific tone.

If the roads are wet and muddy,
We remain at home and study,—
For the Goat is very clever at a sum,—
And the Dog, instead of fighting,
Studies ornamental writing,
While the Cat is taking lessons on the drum.

We retire at eleven,
And we rise again at seven;
And I wish to call attention, as I close,
To the fact that all the scholars
Are correct about their collars,
And particular in turning out their toes.

The Table and the Chair

Edward Lear

Said the Table to the Chair,
"You can hardly be aware
How I suffer from the heat
And from chilblains on my feet.
If we took a little walk,
We might have a little talk;
Pray let us take the air,"
Said the Table to the Chair.

Said the Chair unto the Table,
"Now, you *know* we are not able:
How foolishly you talk,
When you know we *cannot* walk!"
Said the Table with a sigh,
"It can do no harm to try.
I've as many legs as you:
Why can't we walk on two?"

So they both went slowly down,
And walked about the town
With a cheerful bumpy sound
As they toddled round and round;
And everybody cried,
As they hastened to their side,
"See! the Table and the Chair
Have come out to take the air!"

But in going down an alley
To a castle in a valley,
They completely lost their way,
And wandered all the day;

Till, to see them safely back,
They paid a Ducky-quack,
And a Beetle, and a Mouse,
Who took them to their house.

Then they whispered to each other,
"O delightful little brother,
What a lovely walk we've taken!
Let us dine on beans and bacon."
So the Ducky and the leetle
Browny-Mousy and the Beetle
Dined, and danced upon their heads
Till they toddled to their beds.

A Nautical Ballad

Charles Edward Carryl

A capital ship for an ocean trip,
  Was "The Walloping Window-Blind;"
No gale that blew dismayed her crew,
  Nor troubled the captain's mind.

The man at the wheel was taught to feel
  Contempt for the wildest blow;
And it often appeared—when the weather
  had cleared—
  He had been in his bunk below.

The boatswain's mate was very sedate,
Yet fond of amusement, too;
And he played hopscotch with the starboard
watch,
While the captain tickled the crew.

And the gunner we had was apparently mad,
For he sat on the after-rail
And fired salutes with the captain's boots
In the teeth of the booming gale.

The captain sat on the commodore's hat,
And dined, in a royal way,
Off toasted pigs and pickles and figs
And gummery bread each day.

The cook was Dutch and behaved as such,
For the diet he gave the crew
Was a number of tons of hot-cross buns,
Served up with sugar and glue.

All nautical pride we laid aside,
And we cast our vessel ashore,
On the Gulliby Isles, where the Poo-Poo
smiles
And the Rumpletum-Bunders roar

We sat on the edge of a sandy ledge,
And shot at the whistling bee:
And the cinnamon bats wore waterproof hats,
As they danced by the sounding sea.

On Rug-gub bark, from dawn till dark,
We fed, till we all had grown
Uncommonly shrunk—when a Chinese junk
Came in from the Torriby Zone.

She was stubby and square, but we didn't much care,
So we cheerily put to sea;
And we left the crew of the junk to chew
The bark of the Rug-gub tree.

A Goblinade

Florence Page Jaques

A green hobgoblin,
Small but quick,
Went out walking
With a black thorn stick.

He was full of mischief,
  Full of glee.
He frightened all
  That he could see.

He saw a little maiden
  In a wood.
He looked as fierce as
  A goblin should.

He crept by the hedge row,
  He said, "Boo!"
"Boo!" laughed the little girl,
  "How are you?"

"What!" said the goblin,
  "Aren't you afraid?"
"I think you're funny,"
  Said the maid.

"Ha!" said the goblin,
  Sitting down flat.
"You think I'm funny?
  I don't like that.

"I'm very frightening.
  You should flee!"

"You're cunning," she said,
"As you can be!"

Then she laughed again, and
Went away.
But the goblin stood there
All that day.

A beetle came by, and
"Well?" it said.
But the goblin only
Shook his head.

"For I am funny,"
He said to it.
"I thought I was alarming,
And I'm not a bit.

"If I'm amusing,"
He said to himself,
"I won't be a goblin,
I'll be an elf!

"For a goblin must be goblin
All the day,
But an elf need only
Dance and play."

So the little green goblin
Became an elf.
And he dances all day, and
He likes himself.

The Frog

Hilaire Belloc

Be kind and tender to the Frog,
  And do not call him names,
As "Slimy-skin," or "Polly-wog,"
  Or likewise "Uncle James,"
Or "Gape-a-grin," or "Toad-gone-wrong,"
  Or "Billy-Bandy Knees":
The frog is justly sensitive
  To epithets like these.

No animal will more repay
  A treatment kind and fair,
At least so lonely people say
Who keep a frog (and by the way,
  They are extremely rare).

The Yak

Hilaire Belloc

As a friend to the children commend me the Yak.
  You will find it exactly the thing:
It will carry and fetch, you can ride on its back,
  Or lead it about with a string.

The Tartar who dwells on the plains of Thibet
  (A desolate region of snow)
Has for centuries made it a nursery pet,
  And surely the Tartar should know!

Then tell your papa where the Yak can be got,
  And if he is awfully rich
He will buy you the creature—or else he will not.
  (I cannot be positive which.)

The Lion

Hilaire Belloc

The Lion, the Lion, he dwells in the waste,
He has a big head and a very small waist;
But his shoulders are stark, and his jaws they are
  grim,
And a good little child will not play with him.

The Gnu

Hilaire Belloc

G. stands for Gnu, whose weapons of defence
Are long, sharp, curling horns, and common-
sense.
To these he adds a name so short and strong,
That even hardy Boers pronounce it wrong.
How often on a bright autumnal day
The pious people of Pretoria say
"Come, let us hunt the—" then no more is heard,
But sounds of strong men struggling with a word;
Meanwhile the distant Gnu with grateful eyes
Observes his opportunity and flies.

The Purple Cow

Gelett Burgess

I never saw a purple cow,
I never hope to see one.
But this I will say anyhow
I'd rather see than be one.

Part III

Trees

Joyce Kilmer

I think that I shall never see
A poem lovely as a tree.
A tree whose hungry mouth is prest
Against the earth's sweet flowing breast;
A tree that looks at God all day,
And lifts her leafy arms to pray;
A tree that may in summer wear
A nest of robins in her hair;
Upon whose bosom snow has lain;
Who intimately lives with rain.
Poems are made by fools like me,
But only God can make a tree.

The Fifteen Acres

James Stephens

I cling and swing
On a branch, or sing
Through the cool, clear hush of Morning, O:
Or fling my wing
On the air, and bring
To sleepier birds a warning, O:

That the night's in flight,
And the sun's in sight,
And the dew is the grass adorning, O:
And the green leaves swing
As I sing, sing, sing,
Up by the river,
Down the dell,
To the little wee nest,
Where the big tree fell,
So early in the morning, O.

I flit and twit
In the sun for a bit
When his light so bright is shining, O:
Or sit and fit
My plumes, or knit
Straw plaits for the nest's nice lining, O:
And she with glee
Shows unto me
Underneath her wings reclining, O:
And I sing that Peg
Has an egg, egg, egg,
Up by the oat-field,
Round the mill,

Past the meadow,
Down by the hill,
So early in the morning, O.

I stoop and swoop
On the air, or loop
Through the trees, and then go soaring, O:
To group with a troop
On the gusty poop
While the wind behind is roaring, O:
I skim and swim
By a cloud's red rim
And up to the azure flooring, O:
And my wide wings drip
As I slip, slip, slip
Down through the rain-drops,
Back where Peg
Broods in the nest
On the little white egg,
So early in the morning, O.

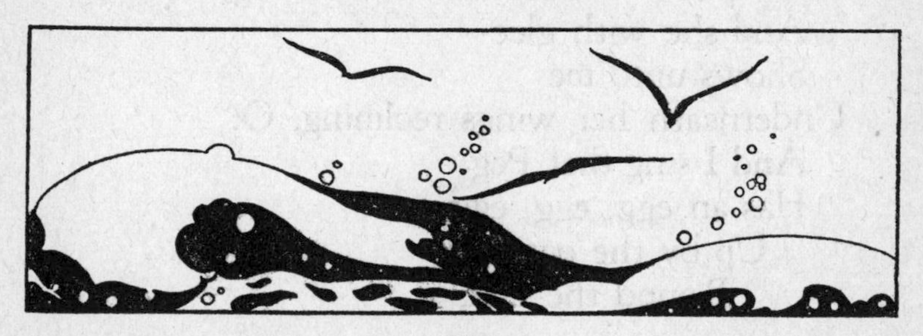

Washington

Nancy Byrd Turner

He played by the river when he was young,
He raced with rabbits along the hills,
He fished for minnows, and climbed and swung,
And hooted back at the whippoorwills.
Strong and slender and tall he grew
And then, one morning, the bugles blew.

Over the hills, the summons came,
Over the river's shining rim.
He said that the bugles called his name,
He knew that his country needed him,
And he answered, "Coming!" and marched away
For many a night and many a day.

Perhaps when the marches were hot and long
He'd think of the river flowing by,
Or, camping under the winter sky,
Would hear the whippoorwill's far-off song.
Boy and soldier, in peace or strife,
He loved America all his life!

Lincoln

Nancy Byrd Turner

There was a boy of other days,
A quiet, awkward, earnest lad,
Who trudged long weary miles to get
A book on which his heart was set—
And then no candle had!

He was too poor to buy a lamp
But very wise in woodmen's ways.
He gathered seasoned bough and stem,
And crisping leaf, and kindled them
Into a ruddy blaze.

Then as he lay full length and read,
The firelight flickered on his face,
And etched his shadow on the gloom,
And made a picture in the room,
In that most humble place.

The hard years came, the hard years went,
But, gentle, brave, and strong of will,
He met them all. And when today
We see his pictured face, we say,
"There's light upon it still."

Interior

Padraic Colum

The little moths are creeping
  Across the cottage pane;
On the floor the chickens gather,
  And they make talk and complain.

And she sits by the fire
  Who has reared so many men;
Her voice is low like the chickens'
  With the things she says again.

"The sons that come back do be restless,
  They search for the thing to say;
Then they take thought like the swallows,
  And the morrow brings them away.

"In the old, old days, upon Innish,
  The fields were lucky and bright,
And if you lay down you'd be covered
  By the grass of one soft night."

She speaks and the chickens gather,
  And they make talk and complain,
While the little moths are creeping
  Across the cottage pane.

The West Wind

John Masefield

It's a warm wind, the west wind, full of birds' cries;
I never hear the west wind but tears are in my eyes.
For it comes from the west lands, the old brown hills,
And April's in the west wind and daffodils.
It's fine land, the west land, for hearts as tired as mine,
Apple orchards blossom there, and the air's like wine.
There is cool green grass there, where men may lie at rest,
And the thrushes are in song there, fluting from the nest.
"Will you not come home, brother? You have been long away,
It's April, and blossom time, and white is the spray;
And bright is the sun, brother, and warm is the rain,—
Will you not come home, brother, home to us again?

The young corn is green, brother, where the
rabbits run;
It's blue sky, and white clouds, and warm
rain and sun.
It's song to a man's soul, brother, fire to a
man's brain,
To hear the wild bees and see the merry
spring again.

Larks are singing in the west, brother, above
the green wheat,
So will you not come home, brother, and
rest your tired feet?
I've a balm for bruised hearts, brother, sleep
for aching eyes,"
Says the warm wind, the west wind, full of
birds' cries.

It's the white road westwards is the road I
must tread
To the green grass, the cool grass, and rest
for heart and head,
To the violets and the brown brooks and the
thrushes' song,
In the fine land, the west land, the land
where I belong.

Silver Ships

Mildred Plew Merryman

There are trails that a lad may follow
  When the years of his boyhood slip,
But I shall soar like a swallow
  On the wings of a silver ship,

Guiding my bird of metal,
  One with her throbbing frame,
Floating down like a petal,
  Roaring up like a flame;

Winding the wind that scatters
  Smoke from the chimney's lip,
Tearing the clouds to tatters
  With the wings of a silver ship;

Grazing the broad blue sky light
  Up where the falcons fare,
Riding the realms of twilight,
  Brushed by a comet's hair;

Snug in my coat of leather,
  Watching the skyline swing,
Shedding the world like a feather
  From the tip of a tilted wing.

There are trails that a lad may travel
When the years of his boyhood wane,
But I'll let a rainbow ravel
Through the wings of my silver plane.

Loveliest of Trees

A. E. Housman

Loveliest of trees, the cherry now
Is hung with bloom along the bough,
And stands about the woodland ride
Wearing white for Eastertide.

Now, of my threescore years and ten,
Twenty will not come again,
And take from seventy springs a score,
It only leaves me fifty more.

And since to look at things in bloom
Fifty springs are little room,
About the woodlands I will go
To see the cherry hung with snow.

Splinter

Carl Sandburg

The voice of the last cricket
across the first frost
is one kind of good-by.
It is so thin a splinter of singing.

The Lake Isle of Innisfree

William Butler Yeats

I will arise and go now, and go to Innisfree,
And a small cabin build there, of clay and
wattles made;
Nine bean rows will I have there, a hive for
the honey bee,
And live alone in the bee-loud glade.

And I shall have some peace there, for peace
comes dropping slow,
Dropping from the veils of the morning to
where the cricket sings;
There midnight's all a glimmer, and noon
a purple glow,
And evening full of the linnet's wings.

I will arise and go now, for always night
and day
I hear lake water lapping with low sounds
by the shore;
While I stand on the roadway, or on the
pavements gray,
I hear it in the deep heart's core.

Some One

Walter de la Mare

Some one came knocking
  At my wee, small door;
Some one came knocking,
  I'm sure—sure—sure;
I listened, I opened,
  I looked to left and right,
But nought there was a-stirring
  In the still dark night.
Only the busy beetle
  Tap-tapping in the wall,
Only from the forest
  The screech-owl's call,
Only the cricket whistling
  While the dewdrops fall,
So I know not who came knocking,
  At all, at all, at all.

Stopping by Woods on a Snowy Evening

Robert Frost

Whose woods these are I think I know.
His house is in the village though;
He will not see me stopping here
To watch his woods fill up with snow.

The little horse must think it queer
To stop without a farmhouse near
Between the woods and frozen lake
The darkest evening of the year.

He gives his harness bells a shake
To ask if there is some mistake.
The only other sound's the sweep
Of easy wind and downy flake.

The woods are lovely dark and deep.
But I have promises to keep,
And miles to go before I sleep,
And miles to go before I sleep.

Columbus

Joaquin Miller

Behind him lay the grey Azores,
  Behind the Gates of Hercules;
Before him not the ghost of shores,
  Before him only shoreless seas.
The good mate said: "Now must we pray,
  For lo! the very stars are gone.
Brave Admiral, speak, what shall I say?"
  "Why, say 'Sail on! sail on! and on!' "

"My men grow mutinous day by day;
  My men grow ghastly wan and weak."
The stout mate thought of home; a spray
  Of salt wave washed his swarthy cheek.
"What shall I say, brave Admiral, say,
  If we sight naught but seas at dawn?"
"Why, you shall say at break of day,
  'Sail on! sail on! sail on! and on!' "

They sailed and sailed, as winds might blow,
  Until at last the blanched mate said,
"Why, now not even God would know
  Should I and all my men fall dead.

These very winds forget their way,
   For God from these dread seas is gone.
Now speak, brave Admiral, speak and say"—
   He said: "Sail on! sail on! and on!"

They sailed. They sailed. Then spake the mate:
   "This mad sea shows his teeth tonight.
He curls his lips, he lies in wait,
   With lifted teeth, as if to bite!
Brave Admiral, say but one good word:
   What shall we do when hope is gone?"
The words leapt like a leaping sword:
   "Sail on! sail on! sail on! and on!"

Then, pale and worn, he kept his deck,
   And peered through darkness. Ah, that night
Of all dark nights! And then a speck—
   A light! a light! a light! a light!
It grew, a starlit flag unfurled!
   It grew to be Time's burst of dawn.
He gained a world; he gave that world
   Its grandest lesson: "On, sail on!"

A Song of Sherwood

Alfred Noyes

Sherwood in the twilight, is Robin Hood awake?
Grey and ghostly shadows are gliding through the brake,
Shadows of the dappled deer, dreaming of the morn,
Dreaming of a shadowy man that winds a shadowy horn.

Robin Hood is here again: all his merry thieves
Hear a ghostly bugle-note shivering through the leaves,
Calling as he used to call, faint and far away,
In Sherwood, in Sherwood, about the break of day.

Merry, merry England has kissed the lips of June;
All the wings of fairyland were here beneath the moon,
Like a flight of rose-leaves fluttering in a mist
Of opal and ruby and pearl and amethyst.

Merry, merry England is waking as of old,
With eyes of blither hazel and hair of brighter gold;
For Robin Hood is here again beneath the bursting spray
In Sherwood, in Sherwood, about the break of day.

Love is in the greenwood building him a house
Of wild rose and hawthorn and honey-suckle boughs;
Love is in the greenwood, dawn is in the skies,
And Marian is waiting with a glory in her eyes.

Hark! The dazzled laverock climbs the golden steep!
Marian is waiting; is Robin Hood asleep?
Round the fairy grass-rings frolic elf and fay,
In Sherwood, in Sherwood, about the break of day.

Oberon, Oberon, rake away the gold,
Rake away the red leaves, roll away the
mould,
Rake away the gold leaves, roll away the
red,
And wake Will Scarlett from his leafy forest bed.

Friar Tuck and Little John are riding down
together
With quarter-staff and drinking-can and
grey goose-feather.
The dead are coming back again, the years
are rolled away
In Sherwood, in Sherwood, about the break
of day.

Softly over Sherwood the south wind blows.
All the heart of England hid in every rose
Hears across the greenwood the sunny
whisper leap,
Sherwood in the red dawn, is Robin Hood
asleep?

Hark, the voice of England wakes him as of old
And, shattering the silence with a cry of brighter gold,
Bugles in the greenwood echo from the steep,
Sherwoood in the red dawn, is Robin Hood asleep?

Where the deer are gliding down the shadowy glen
All across the glades of fern he calls his merry men—
Doublets of the Lincoln green glancing through the May
In Sherwood, in Sherwood, about the break of day—

Calls them and they answer: from aisles of oak and ash
Rings the *Follow! Follow!* and the boughs begin to crash,
The ferns begin to flutter and the flowers begin to fly,
And through the crimson dawning the robber band goes by.

Robin! Robin! Robin! All her merry thieves
Answer as the bugle-note shivers through
the leaves,
Calling as he used to call, faint and far away,
In Sherwood, in Sherwood, about the break
of day.

America For Me

Henry van Dyke

'Tis fine to see the Old World, and travel up
and down
Among the famous palaces and cities of renown,
To admire the crumbly castles and the stat-
ues of the kings,—
But now I think I've had enough of anti-
quated things

*So it's home again, and home again, Amer-
ica for me!*
*My heart is turning home again, and there I
long to be,*
*In the land of youth and freedom beyond
the ocean bars,*
*Where the air is full of sunlight and the flag
is full of stars.*

Oh, London is a man's town, there's power
in the air;
And Paris is a woman's town, with flowers
in her hair;
And it's sweet to dream in Venice, and it's
great to study Rome;
But when it comes to living there is no place
like home.

I like the German fir-woods, in green batta-
lions drilled;
I like the gardens of Versailles with flashing
fountains filled;
But, oh, to take your hand, my dear, and
ramble for a day
In the friendly western woodland where
Nature has her way!

I know that Europe's wonderful, yet some-
thing seems to lack:
The Past is too much with her, and the peo-
ple looking back.
But the glory of the Present is to make the
Future free,—
We love our land for what she is and what
she is to be.

Oh, it's nome again, and home again, America for me!
I want a ship that's westward bound to plough the rolling sea,
To the blessed Land of Room Enough beyond the ocean bars,
Where the air is full of sunlight and the flag is full of stars.

America the Beautiful

Katharine Lee Bates

O beautiful for spacious skies,
For amber waves of grain,
For purple mountain majesties
Above the fruited plain!
America! America!
God shed His grace on thee
And crown thy good with brotherhood
From sea to shining sea!

O beautiful for pilgrim feet,
Whose stern, impassioned stress
A thoroughfare for freedom beat
Across the wilderness!
America! America!
God mend thine every flaw,
Confirm thy soul in self-control,
Thy liberty in law!

O beautiful for heroes proved
In liberating strife,
Who more than self their country loved,
And mercy more than life!
America! America!
May God thy gold refine
Till all success be nobleness
And every gain divine!

O beautiful for patriot dream
That sees beyond the years
Thine alabaster cities gleam
Undimmed by human tears!
America! America!
God shed His grace on thee
And crown thy good with brotherhood
From sea to shining sea!

I Never Saw a Moor

Emily Dickinson

I never saw a moor,
I never saw the sea;
Yet know I how the heather looks,
And what a wave must be.

I never spoke with God,
Nor visited in heaven;
Yet certain am I of the spot
As if the chart were given.

Time, You Old Gipsy Man

Ralph Hodgson

Time, you old gipsy man,
  Will you not stay,
Put up your caravan
  Just for one day?

All things I'll give you
Will you be my guest,
Bells for your jennet
Of silver the best,

Goldsmiths shall beat you
A great golden ring,
Peacocks shall bow to you,
Little boys sing.
Oh, and sweet girls will
Festoon you with may,
Time, you old gipsy,
Why hasten away?
Last week in Babylon,
Last night in Rome,
Morning, and in the crush
Under Paul's dome;
Under Paul's dial
You tighten your rein—
Only a moment,
And off once again;
Off to some city
Now blind in the womb,
Off to another
Ere that's in the tomb.

Time, you old gipsy,
Will you not stay,
Put up your caravan
Just for one day?

Sea-Fever

John Masefield

I must go down to the seas again, to the
lonely sea and the sky,
And all I ask is a tall ship and a star to steer
her by,
And the wheel's kick and the wind's song
and the white sail's shaking,
And a grey mist on the sea's face and a grey
dawn breaking.

I must go down to the seas again, for the
call of the running tide
Is a wild call and a clear call that may not
be denied;
And all I ask is a windy day with the white
clouds flying,
And the flung spray and the blown spume,
and the sea-gulls crying.

I must go down to the seas again to the
vagrant gypsy life,
To the gull's way and the whale's way where
the wind's like a whetted knife;
And all I ask is a merry yarn from a laughing
fellow-rover,
And quiet sleep and a sweet dream when
the long trick's over.

Frolic

A. E.

The children were shouting together
And racing along the sands,
A glimmer of dancing shadows,
A dovelike flutter of hands.

The stars were shouting in heaven,
The sun was chasing the moon:
The game was the same as the children's,
They danced to the self-same tune.

The whole of the world was merry,
One joy from the vale to the height,
Where the blue woods of twilight encircled
The lovely lawns of the light.

The Linnet

Walter de la Mare

Upon this leafy bush
With thorns and roses in it,
Flutters a thing of light,
A twittering linnet.

And all the throbbing world
   Of dew and sun and air
By this small parcel of life
   Is made more fair;
As if each bramble-spray
And mounded gold-wreathed furze,
   Harebell and little thyme,
   Were only hers;
As if this beauty and grace
   Did to one bird belong,
And, at a flutter of wing,
   Might vanish in song.

A Psalm of Praise

Psalm 100

Make a joyful noise unto the Lord, all ye lands.
Serve the Lord with gladness; come before his presence with singing.
Know ye that the Lord he is God: it is he that hath made us, and not we ourselves: we are his people, and the sheep of his pasture.
Enter into his gates with thanksgiving, and into his courts with praise: be thankful unto him and bless his name.
For the Lord is good; his mercy is everlasting; and his truth endureth to all generations.

CONTENTS